RIDES AGAIN

by Russell Myers

**tempo
books**
GROSSET & DUNLAP
A Filmways Company
Publishers • New York

ISBN: 0-448-17130-9

Tempo Books is Registered in the U.S. Patent Office
A Tempo Books Original
Published Simultaneously in Canada

Printed in the United States of America

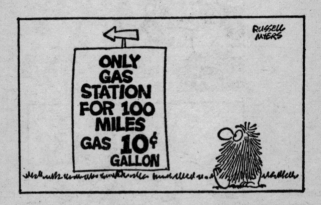

THE GREAT
DEVELOPMENT WAR

RUSSELL MYERS

3/12

2/13

RUSSELL
MYERS

CATALOG SALES

RUSSELL MYERS

3/4

3/14

RUSSELL MYERS

RUSSELL MYERS

5/27

RUSSELL MYERS

6/18